NOON

Editor	DIANE WILLIAMS
Consulting Editor	CHRISTINE SCHUTT
Senior Editors	RACHEL CHAIT
	ZACH DAVIDSON
	MADELAINE LUCAS
	LIZA ST. JAMES
Assistant Editors	WILL AUGEROT
	DANIEL FELSENTHAL
	ROBERT IRISH
	MARK TESHIROGI
	JEFF WEINSTEIN
	CECILE YAMA
Contributing Editors	REBEKAH BERGMAN
	KAYLA BLATCHLEY
	ENA BRDJANOVIC
	RITA BULLWINKEL
	HILARY LEICHTER
	NADXIELI NIETO
	MARY SOUTH
	LAUREN SPOHRER
Production Editor	WILL AUGEROT
Designer	SUSAN CARROLL
Development Director	RICK WHITAKER
Copy Editor	CAITLIN VAN DUSEN
Directors	BILL HAYWARD
	LAURA KIRK
	CHRISTINE SCHUTT
	DAVID SLATER
	HAMZA WALKER
	DIANE WILLIAMS

NOON is an independent not-for-profit literary annual published by NOON, Inc.

Edition price $15.00 (domestic) or $20.00 (foreign)
All donations are tax deductible.

⟷

NOON is distributed by ANC, 1955 Lake Park Drive #400, Smyrna, Georgia 30080
(800) 929-8274, and Media Solutions, 9632 Madison Boulevard, Madison,
Alabama 35758 (800) 476-5872

NOON welcomes submissions. Send to:
Diane Williams
NOON, 1392 Madison Avenue, PMB 298, New York, New York 10029
Please include the necessary self-addressed, stamped envelope.
We do not accept international reply coupons.
noonannual.com

ISSN 1526-8055
© 2022 by NOON, Inc.
All rights reserved *Printed in U.S.A.*

NOON is indexed by *Humanities International Complete.*
Cover design by Susan Carroll. Cover: *Tom in Albisola*, 2020. Inside: *Metropolitan*, 2019.
Both by Louis Fratino. Courtesy of the artist and Sikkema Jenkins & Co.

CONTENTS

The Editors proudly congratulate Kathryn Scanlan,
recipient of the 2021 Literature Award from the
American Academy of Arts and Letters.

The Editors proudly congratulate Stephen Mortland,
recipient of a 2022 Pushcart Prize for his story "Elenin,"
which appeared in the 2020 edition of *NOON*.

The Editors proudly congratulate Vijay Khurana, who won the
2021 *Griffith Review* Emerging Voices Competition and was
shortlisted for the 2021 Bristol Short Story Prize (UK).

MEDITATION

KATHRYN SCANLAN

When I wake up I brew a little pot of tea and when it's ready I pour it into my favorite cup, which is thin-walled and not very large. I pour the tea until it reaches the top of the cup and then I pour a little more up above the brim—I want one of those tight, trembling, difficult domes. I want more than my cup can hold.

Later I do it with purée from the blender pitcher, and in the evening I do it with wine.

I reflect on how far I've come and how far I have yet to go in my world made cunningly.

INTELLIGENCE AND BLOOD

KATHRYN SCANLAN

The baby didn't cry. Her mother checked on her often to make sure she was alive. Sometimes the baby's skin looked blue, like a baby in a snowbank, a baby stuck in a block of ice. I want to play with her—when will she wake up? asked her mother, who was scolded by her sisters, girlfriends, neighbors, mother, and husband for failing to recognize her good luck.

A few years passed. The baby became a toddler and the toddler became a schoolchild. She didn't eat much, was small for her age. She had frequent fevers and was force-fed spoonfuls of milky pink medicine from amber bottles. She slept twelve, fifteen hours a day. One afternoon, during recess, she was shoved from a high playground perch and landed on her chin, which split open and soaked her shirt with blood. She bit through her tongue too.

When she opened her mouth to speak, blood poured out. She asked: Will I die now? She looked surprised—disappointed?—by the doctor's answer.

In the years that followed she had a perpetual lump in her throat that she could neither swallow nor spit up. When she ate, the lump tried to choke her. When she didn't eat, the lump throbbed. When she spoke, the lump weakened her voice—people had to lean in, ask, What?

When she turned eighteen, she went with some friends on a canoe trip in a northerly region famous for its enormous mosquitoes. On the third day, sunburnt and sick of each other, the girl and her friends arrived at a bend in the river—a deep pool that people were diving into from a rocky overhang. They dragged their canoes onto the bank and climbed the cliff.

One, two, three—the girl watched her friends jump and land laughing below. But at the edge, she stopped, tripped—hit a branch on the way down. She landed flat on the water—face-first—and blacked out.

When she was revived on the shore, she had two broken teeth, two black eyes, a split lip, a full-body bruise. Her head felt cracked and when she spoke blood leaked from her mouth. She was loaded into her canoe and paddled by her partners downriver toward their destination, which was still several hours away.

The girl sat and watched the oily water part at the prow of the boat. Farther along, the sun was doing its bronzing work, and above their heads, swarms of small birds were swallowing bugs in flight. She felt deeply hungry and was grateful for the thick iron taste in her mouth. She laughed and spat out a chunk of tooth.

Along the banks grew a type of tree that looks to some like a sorrowful woman whose long hair falls forward from her head in grief, but to the girl the trees seemed to plunge happily—greedily—into the river and take from it what they needed.

HOW DO YOU DO

CHRISTINE SCHUTT

The four-poster double bed from the redbrick house took up most of the new bedroom, and Mother took up most of the old bed, lying across it, loose and lascivious. I had to press against the wall to get around to the far side of the bed for my own space from which to visit her. Another woman sat in a club chair I didn't recognize, but which took up the other side. We were introduced. She was a new friend, a new admirer of Mother's—I should have been paying attention, but I was flummoxed to think the bed, the chair, the dresser were all that was left of the old house I grew up in. Also, more to the point, I didn't like Mother's ardent new acquaintances.

I liked the old friends, the courtesy aunts of our youth, but my brother had told me they didn't come around anymore, or rarely. This new woman, Ann, I think, was visibly disappointed by my intrusion; because of me, whatever intimacy that might have caught fire at Mother's bedside was extinguished.

Two o'clock in the afternoon and Mother half-dressed for something dressy: a drapey navy blouse, unbuttoned, and navy hose that smudged her sex and made her long legs look dirty.

All of her attention was on me.

"What are you wearing?" she asked.

Ann stood up and introduced herself. This time I heard the name, surely a nickname, Zan.

Mother looked to Zan and then to me again, all the while touching herself lightly until I pulled the sheet over her legs.

"What?"

"You look as if you were dressing to go out," I said.

"What?"

"The pretty blouse, nylons. Were you going out?"

Mother looked at Zan. "Were we?" she asked, and she made deliberate laughing sounds, but she was not exactly laughing, which confused Zan—and me. After a while, Mother said, yes, they had thought about it, lunch, but I already knew what lunch meant, a restaurant somewhere with a bar.

Would Mother drink in front of Zan? How much did Zan know?

I let Mother drink every time. I'd do so again.

"You don't look too mobile," I said to her.

She said, "I'm not. I've had a fright. Something's happening to me"—a familiar phrase auguring ill. "I can't read anymore."

She appeared astonished. She said, "Literally. I literally cannot read a page. I can make out the letters, but the sentences make no sense, the page is a kind of blank to me, and I love to read." She said, "Zan will tell you. She's had to read to me!" Mother clenched and unclenched her hands.

"I have no memory of what happened yesterday or the year before. It's as if the back door to where the old events are stored is shut to me. I'm locked out of everything that's happened." She went on with her kind of hand-wringing, pulling on her crooked digits.

I hadn't seen her in months. I had only just arrived and gone from airport to hotel to here, her new home. My brother had found it, this room with a bathroom and somewhere a closet. Ivy Manor, so-called, semi-independent living in a building attached to a nursing part by an underground chute, or so Ted had described it. Here the unable old were simply scrolled into pneumatic tubes that hurtled toward a room with furnishings on casters.

Mother had grown up in a house with a library, but perhaps she had forgotten as much.

"Maybe the books you're trying to read are just bad?" I suggested.

She frowned and from under the sheet, she brought out a romance novel with Cardinal Wolsey and a philandering husband, debt and danger.

"The heroine triumphs, I assume."

"I don't know," she said.

"A lot of characters, I bet."

"Impossible," she said. "Zan finds it hard to read too. Don't you?"

Zan appeared uncertain.

Mother said, "At least Zan can read, but the sentences are long and it's easy to lose track . . ."

"I'm not so bad."

"You're not," Mother said. "I'm the one. The marks on the page make as much sense as mouse poop to me. And I drift off."

"We've tried," Zan said, "but things come up, don't they?"

Mother looked at me and asked was I going anywhere, and I saw I had not taken off my coat, and I felt compelled to explain I had only just arrived, bags at the hotel, room not ready.

"Remember the way I came in? I'm grimy!" I said—too vehement. Mother was alarmed, which annoyed Zan, who pointed to a door I had taken for a closet.

"Sal's got a nice bathroom," Zan said.

"How do you know?" Mother asked. "And don't call me Sal, please."

The Zans in Mother's life learned to give way to her— accepted the charges or else called my brother. They knew where the keys were kept and the overnight suitcase; they knew what to pack for whatever came next. A list of her meds and emergency numbers, her address book and calendar. Her end-of-life directives.

But this Zan was a new acquaintance.

This Zan had yet to learn my mother expected formality even if she was fingering her twat.

Zan looked at her lap, embarrassed.

"About your reading problem," I said to Mother.

She said, "There isn't a cure."

She said my room was probably ready by now, and I should go back to the hotel, unpack, and bathe. "You'll feel better. Order room service. The food's not very good here."

Zan offered to drop me off on her way home, and I accepted the ride.

"Out of your way, isn't it?" Mother asked her.

"Not so much," Zan said, but when she asked about their next date, Mother looked at me, and in the most unfriendly voice said, "My daughter is here."

I felt sorry for Zan then, but not so much as to be particularly friendly.

That night I lay on a bed as big as the room I was in, and I thought of where my mother lay on an equally large bed in an even smaller room where she said it harshly again and again— My daughter is here. My daughter is here.

Years after her death, I still feel sorry for myself, but not so much as to be particularly consoled.

EKALAKA

VI KHI NAO

Some would describe Schuster as soft butch because she wore glittering, leaflet-like earrings and sometimes her body would shape like a bell curve.

I was twenty-three years old then and she was forty-six, exactly twice my age and four years older than my mother. So you can imagine my homophobic parents' reaction when they discovered that I was dating her.

She was a chemist, beekeeper, carpenter, martial arts instructor, and a roofer. I was a baby dyke who was being tossed about and I knew very little about love.

Homophobia had already shaped the primary language of intimacy between us in public, but the age difference added another layer of demurral and negation to our already nonpublic relationship. She kissed me in private and rejected our relationship in public. But before the relationship settled itself in the arena of contempt, impotence, and loss, she invited me to come and visit her in Ekalaka, Montana, during the months when work was slow.

The quadrant barn to her estate was massive. It stood tall like one of those large Victorian houses in *Wuthering Heights*. Inside it, she stored her wooden honey extractor, which she had constructed from scratch with an engineer who used to build commercial airplanes for large companies such as Boeing.

Standing near it, the whole structure looked to me like a makeshift bathroom stall. But the most erotic experience I encountered rurally was watching honey dripping out of the extractor's lips.

Perhaps I shouldn't have been so hard on her for always clothing our homosexuality. Her neighbors were Republicans and simpleminded and they must not have known of our Sapphicity, or they would have ousted her and me too.

She had a black cat named Batman, who, before he committed suicide via rat poisoning, chased me around the cottage with his S-shaped black tail in the air like a panther after an antelope.

I used to believe he would eat me for a midnight snack and I had every reason to believe in the veracity of this assumption.

After my long walks in the alfalfa fields, I would come back to the cottage and find that at the center of the cottage, not too far away from the kitchen table, Batman had torn a rat into two.

Half the rat's body was on the kitchen floor and the other part of it was in the living room, the entrails scattered everywhere.

To widen the landscape of my eyeballs, the following day the superhero cat climbed across several cabinets before capturing a dove in his mouth who had accidently flown in through the window.

Schuster and I never made love properly, meaning innately or inherently. She felt climaxing was an assault on her belief that sex was, in fact, a tool for false intimacy. To avoid pseudo-intimacy, when we fucked she would hypocritically force us to never reach the pinnacle of our mutual ardor.

During the second autumn of my arrival at her rural estate, it snowed so mammothly that the entire town of Ekalaka appeared like a flat version of Mount Everest.

Standing in her bedroom, I could not distinguish land from sky. It was one seamless fabric of a chalky effusion of breath, air, and endless crystal flakes.

One of my favorite memories took place during this visit. A hailstorm had battered her truck and the roofs of her cottage and quadrant barn. It was a quiet afternoon when she helped me climb to her roof using a long ladder so I could inhale the panoramic view of Ekalaka.

I watched her remove the old, hail-torn shingles and nail-gun the new ones. It was peaceful and she was as butch as she could be.

She had once told me a story about an abusive husband who would beat his wife and children. The wife told him that if he laid hands on their children, she would kill him. And she warned him to not wear his boots into their home because she had recently washed the floor, but he paid no heed. Not caring whether he beat her, she nail-gunned his boots to the floor.

Schuster spent the next decade trying to re-court me on and off, but I never want to turn into a pillar of salt.

IN WITH OUR WHOLE BODIES

LUCIE ELVEN

I was annoyingly enigmatic. Eric was harsh in a nice way. I wondered what would happen if we went in further.

I was the one who had asked to meet. I was always the one, and I confess I imagined sex that was like a long scream.

When I called, he assured me that the improbable gap in the trees was the correct entrance and I made my way through long grass and flowers to try to find him. The building had once been an asylum, and was now converted into apartments. Eric's kitchen doors led into the garden where someone—him? where was his housemate?—had laid down a woolen blanket.

My good friend Louise Marshall had been the reason I arrived late. If Eric had been late, I would have killed him. But as it was, I was the late one, and he, or someone, had already arranged the picnic.

I remembered the housemate—what was her name?—serving me dinner at their previous home. I had recently been to a region where she had never been. "The line of the mountains. . . ," I had explained to her. "It's very particular there." I had gotten out my phone and searched for an image that would illustrate the point. I'd cocked my wrist at her over the table. "There, you see, a very particular shape. A shape you don't see often."

Today I found an opening around the side of the compound, a tree providing an arch and, under some ivy, leaves—a passage to nowhere bookended by brown brick walls. In the other direction, near others eating and talking, a girl was having her hair cut by a slim man with his hair in a bun and long-sleeved clothes.

She waved and she called to Eric, "I sent Gisèle the billet doux!"

"You *what?*" Eric shouted. His voice and specifically his laugh—it was different. It was more in the back of his throat, hollow. He had never become unrestrained like that with me.

To me he said he got a greater satisfaction these days from knowing he had turned pleasure away rather than letting it run like cold water down his gullet.

Eric didn't seem to be avoiding me—he had taken his place next to the empty plate destined for me. He led the conversation—what had I been up to, had I adopted a dog yet, were there not certain types of dogs that were less bad for allergies?

"Poodles," I began, but Eric interrupted and pointed to where my eyes were wandering—to the makeshift salon, the hairdresser's final adjustments, the woman with her hair down. She was removing her cape after the cut.

"It's Grace," he explained, pointing at her. "I think you've met."

I looked at the woman before us in the center of the grass, as all of the others around us applauded the hairdresser's work. I felt tricked, like somebody had hidden her from me or led me to believe she was unimportant, a red herring, when she was in fact the murderer, the reason why in bed, soon after, I came several times: first when I was sitting on him, masturbating him like a rocket, like his penis was mine, then again a second time I don't remember, and then when we touched each other before he went to sleep.

I had from the start expected I'd feel horror, and for a minute in my half sleep I did not doubt what I had gotten myself into.

I opened the curtains. Eric was sleeping.

I found some wrapped food on the dresser top. I like cold food better than when it was hot. The tastes are more familiar, worn, the shapes are more curled, cochlear, the stickiness sweeter.

I took reports of Eric back to my friends: "He hadn't washed," or "He was swearing," or "He's put on a lot of weight, I think."

"Is he the alcoholic?" Louise Marshall asked finally.

THE BIKEWORKS

LUCIE ELVEN

The woman I had addressed looked at me with disinterest that was so pronounced I took it as studied interest.

"I have a very ugly bike," she said. "It needs some work. I'll show you."

I stepped out of the shop to follow her as she reluctantly made her way over to a shape in the front row. "You see. It is old and scratched and damaged. But it has a good frame, good vintage features. I like this," she said, running her fingers over the rainbow paintwork, cut through with rust. She said it would be £100.

"Because it isn't so beautiful, it won't get stolen," I said, stammering a bit, as though I was insulting her.

"I was going to paint it," she replied, "but I couldn't be bothered."

She was so unprofessional, so much her inflexible self, that I was impressed. I said I lived just there and could drop by at the end of the week but she took my number and said she would give me a call when she'd fixed the bike up in a couple of days.

A week passed without my hearing from the bike shop woman, so I stopped in. There was a black bike out front. "Is this the one?" I asked, and she said yeah. It was marked £180. I said that the price had gone up.

"I don't know why I didn't call," she mused. "I spray-painted it and did a lot of work."

She looked away at the next customer. She suggested that I take it for a ride around the corner so I got on and turned down a quiet street. The whole bike shuddered at each bump.

"It's good," I said when I returned. I think I was fascinated by how little she'd done. "The only problem is that the handlebars are too low."

She placed the bike between her thighs and proceeded to tug it side to side. I tried to discreetly signal I was a stabilizing influence by holding the rear of the bike down with one hand poking out of my straight black coat. Once she had succeeded in pulling the handlebars up, I said I'd take it.

She looked incredulous, as if it was too soon. "Now?"

"Yes." And it felt good to insist.

The left handlebar is twisted and almost faces the ground, so that you can't use that brake without time to prepare. Nevertheless, I love to speed down the Bethnal Green Road, with its many stops and starts, calling about me all my senses for protection. The old battered and deformed bike with a good frame gets velocity. I can hear a part of it saying, *Let go, let go now.* But unlike a lover who will soon be in another hemisphere, moving freely, so much detached from me, the bike needs me in order to work. I will not be going to sleep happy, thinking that I have convinced my bike to stay, and waking up, knowing it will still be leaving. Whenever it leaves, I will be leaving too.

I thought my sister was helping me while I was cooking, but when I looked up she was playing with her scarf.

So I told her about the time I dropped my phone on the Sapsan train tracks and used the emergency line—about the sight of the next train pulling up slowly, about it stopping just in front of the phone, the driver climbing down the rungs of a ladder to pick it up and hand it to me, a fantasy of support.

My sister held her fists in front of her as she leant back in bliss.

VERY UNDERSTANDABLE

LUCIE ELVEN

Ugly—I am so ugly. My neck is considerable. I caught my own reflection in the mirrored wall of the restaurant.

But in Kate's line of work, I thought, ugliness seems almost an asset. It allows one to be underestimated. It gives one gravitas. It provides necessary self-hatred.

Over the course of the evening, when Kate returned one of my questions to me, she repeated my name in a jocular way, as if she were putting it on a shelf.

Drunk and lying in my bed that night, all I wanted to know was what her face would do if I saw her body naked, finding that several other things had to be happening at once for me to get to where I wanted at the task at hand. With repeated little slapping noises I brought myself close, then, tilting forward, filling and tightening, I pitched over like an anxious voice.

I saw Kate on a city street a few weeks later. The skies were scattered and I was slightly overdressed, as it wasn't cold that day. I felt high up, especially my heart, and slipped a little on the mud. "You. Really?" she said when I stopped her. She didn't wrap her arm around me for long, just lightly touched me, like a dancer reproducing intimate physical contact for an audience. Would I like to have dinner?

I suggested a place but Kate said she would rather cook. Being disagreed with gave me a rush. I raised myself to my full height.

The rows of houses I passed as we walked to dinner were traditional and black-lined, cottage-like. I knew that the citizens were extremely proud of their features, their relative smallness was characteristic of their era, but they were charmless to me. So we managed to invent our friendship there in the most absent and bland of circumstances.

I am always asking Kate simplistic, reckless questions about our future together and watching her divide an answer into parts, hoping one of those parts is what I want to hear. I do this even when we are having a good full time sitting together—leaning over and shaking each other by the knees.

I would like to stand: with impatience. I'd be drawn upward by an invisible pinching index and thumb.

I am thinking maybe time has never passed so awkwardly before, or maybe it's always passed just like this, before.

KATE NASH IS BACK

LUCIE ELVEN

Kate Nash who really likes me was back and I could hear her laughing.

A good day had ridden in and I was carousing with old friends. I was enjoying my reputation as a person who has lots of misguided sex, all of it edifying.

I lifted Kate up from behind and she cycled her legs. Once I'd found everything that was knotty, heavy inside her, I felt high pressure ridging in, and a suit of liquid. A human bite was on my arm.

What would happen next?—the nightmare of living comfortably with her and becoming her jealous lover.

I'd be thinking those things alongside her every day, my face more like hers over the years.

The second bite I received that day was from my dog, and it produced four small marks that would unfurl into large black bruises unlike any I'd had before.

On the floor, forgive me for having a bit of a chuckle, I lay back to back with him, his body tightening and filling, mine long, extended, our two spines refusing to fit together.

TO TELL YOU THE TRUTH

LUCIE ELVEN

The only solution was to exclude her from my life. I began employing a businesslike tone, more attentive and undisclosing, as if our messages were being read by a third party. She was cycling toward the conversation where she would be cut off.

She should, I thought, have had the sense to tell someone when the abuse happened; she mightn't have needed therapy. But she was an alluring European. She was volatile, had flyaway hair. She said I made her feel safe.

I'm sorry, I wrote from Florence, from Medina, from Montreal, *that this won't be a longer email*.

Because I'd arrived in Madrid early, I visited the museum.

It's important to be with someone who visits museums at the same pace as you, my mother says. For what it's worth, I like visiting museums half an hour before closing time, running room to room as though I have an urgent appointment in a bed, marching past paintings that, if you made something that good and it took your whole life, it would have been worth it. Stopping with as much certainty before the unexpected.

Will I find my love this way?

PRETTY FLOWER BOY

JAE KIM

The café where I worked summers overlooked the laundresses on the riverbank of the yesteryear village. They rinsed their clothes in the stream and laid them over a slick boulder. They squatted with their feet apart and beat the clothes using short, heavy bats. The pipes they smoked rested beside their hips on the dry pebbles. I went out in the morning and enjoyed the riverbank as much as I could before they arrived, lifting their long skirts to walk, their baskets secure on their heads.

"Hey, Kkonminam," a woman said to a boy in his swim trunks, who handed his dirty clothes to his older sister. "Aren't you too old to be coming to the river?"

Kkonminam, which meant a "pretty flower boy," was, in the

village, a compliment paid to eligible bachelors of girlish complexion.

"I told you," his sister said. Still a young girl but as responsible as any woman, she went door to door selling cakes that she made from rice and bran.

"Hey, Kkonminam," a woman said, "if you keep coming back, the Madame will see that you're hanging around the women at the river when you already have hair on your face."

"Where?" a woman beside him said, lifting his chin.

"You might like the attention these women give you, but they won't be adoring you for much longer," his sister said, beating his clothes. "You'd best get out while you're ahead."

The younger children who didn't like to get wet played house behind the women. They let the babies down from their backs and used the swaddles as tablecloths. They drank "coffee" from pebbles and fed each other rocks. "Open up. Ahhh."

"Ahhh."

The boy's sister took out a box of cigarettes from her sleeve.

"The cake girl is all grown and sucking on cigarettes."

"Look at Kkonminam. He wants what his sister has."

The boy's sister remained merciless. "He heard somewhere about a hand reaching up from inside the toilet," she said. "But who told him this, hmm?" She turned to the children, who giggled. "He was too afraid to use the bathroom at night and I was going to let him cry like a baby at first, but then he got constipated. The doctor gave me a laxative, and when I pulled down the boy's pants to squeeze the laxative between his cheeks, what do I see? A hair sprouting from his anus."

The women didn't hold back their laughter and a laundress said, "I was married before any hair grew between my butts." The boy's sister offered him her cigarette. "Do you see now? You can't come to the river anymore."

The café was where the then Madame, a part-time sibyl, once predicted that I, a little girl at the time, would grow up to take her job in the café. Here I was now, playing records on a turntable, dressed in hanbok. The dust in the light stuck to people's hats, which they insisted on wearing indoors. The sofas were comfortably cushioned, floral patterned. I brewed coffee on the furnace and watered the palm trees.

I cleared the ashtrays and tried to be witty on behalf of my patrons. When the shop owner next door wanted to walk up and down the streets, I kept an eye on the goods, which included cheap jewelry and postcards, including one that I liked of a woman on a tatami floor, playing a stringed instrument on her lap—a black zither?—facing the camera without smiling.

Boys from the nearby neighborhoods came in crowds, but they didn't stay for long, intimidated by the adult conversations around the room. The ones who came alone waited until the late afternoon to come, until after the lunchtime rush and before they needed to be home.

They looked as old as I was, but these boys were intimidated nonetheless, and their friends weren't there to tell them, "You idiot!" when they missed the obvious cues, such as when I sat in front of them and asked what they were reading. They all had book covers, as if to hide their taste in literature. They were very polite, took their hats off to bow, but they refused to look up from their books and finished their cafés au lait as fast as they could.

Some boys followed me home, hiding behind utility poles. I knew these boys, these boys who thought kissing meant French-kissing and whined in their diaries about their own ugly faces. These boys who longed to bear the weight of your body, who made plans to disappear with you to the ends of the earth. These boys who grew up on their sisters' backs and wanted you to rock them to sleep.

A boy two years below me in school used to find me during lunchtime, whether I was on the roof or on the playground benches. He insisted on being beside me, though he never made a move. He would wait by my shoe locker after school and, on rainy days, offer me an umbrella without fail.

There had been a boy who took me to see the stars. To his credit, he didn't give the constellations fake names or spin romantic tales. He'd held a few naive capitalist beliefs but had been essentially agnostic toward everything except the people's, and his own, independence. He turned out to be a socialist in the making. I heard that after I graduated, he began to carry a mimeograph and served detentions for protesting the government's stance on reparations to Vietnam. He and a handful of other students had, using the school bell as a signal, run out of the classroom chanting.

There had been a boy who held my bony hands and thumbed my dry skin and blue veins. I brought him home when my parents were out, but all we ever did was lie on the living room floor holding hands. I appreciated his patience and persistence, but I didn't care for his self-abasing smiles.

These boys never grew up, a truly unbearable bunch. They crawled in through your window and ate your food. When you told them to quit it, they grew to like being scolded by you. They squeezed your breasts and only then realized they should have pursued a girl of their dreams instead of settling for you. I escaped them by immersing myself in politics, canvassing for candidates I believed in.

The boys in politics were ill-suited for the job, both physically and mentally. When the police saw their round tangerine faces, the fight was lost. They didn't even stay in prison for long, since they added so little to the cause. They told stories of their arrests, and once the excitement wore off, they abandoned their posts.

Men no longer tangerine-faced, their charm only a sour taste in women's mouths, didn't leave their houses if they could help it, except to come to the café and claim their corner tables. They watched the dancing that happened on occasion, and pushed aside their chairs to make room. I played the songs, and couples moved clumsily across the floor, knees bumping. They either clutched each other's hands for support or simply stood and swayed. Friends taught one another what they knew until the old men crawled out of their corners to ask the women onto the floor.

I danced with them when my body grew sore from standing. They didn't care who they were dancing with. They felt my center of gravity and were mindful of my shoulders' orientation. They studied my face to gauge my comfort level. At the end of the dance, they wandered off, no thanks or farewell.

One of the boys I knew visited me every summer, each summer from a different city. I let him nap in the room behind the counter, after which he always wanted to go for a walk. We walked upstream until the river was but a shallow creek, before walking back downstream.

We ran into Kkonminam swirling his pan to suspend the sand and let the gold settle. He would carefully sweep off the sand, letting the water slosh along its rim. Patience was his friend. There was no need to see how much gold there was, the gold would be there at the bottom. Specks would begin to glitter in the sun. Not a lot. Not much money. He would take his sucker bottle and suck up the glitter.

I THOUGHT OF TONY, I THOUGHT OF LISA

MARC TWEED

I am a middle manager with sideburns and a twanged-out Southern accent living alone in a mostly unfurnished townhouse. More simian than porcine but definitely bloated, an unessential overlord in two-tone socks. I work in the hydraulics distribution industry, in a building downtown.

Guess what. There was Tony who sat by me.

And guess what else. There was Lisa, who I could hear on the other side of the cubicle wall reciting numbers.

There were sweaty people in the warehouse who shrank at the sound of my voice, and upstairs, others wearing fancier outfits.

But oh how I longed to live the life of a slot machine, loud and fickle, jerked alive by strange hands, put back into my trance by an accomplishment of poverty or elation. I wanted to live like that until someone decided I wanted nothing of the sort.

I determined to find a way and at lunch I took a walk.

I thought of Tony, I thought of Lisa, I wondered about the whole gang. But only in a way.

I hummed an unfortunate song I knew. Mah-na-mah-na or similar.

I felt the song vibrate in my larynx and I walked in time to it.

I existed, sincerely.

I hunted with my eyes for two hours.

To give you an idea of my surroundings. If I went too far east, the road stopped abruptly, halted by the wide gray highway that had brought me here.

I felt no emotion, which was possibly the point, when I saw the strip of the little beige town again and arrived back at work later than I ever had.

I found the building pleasantly warm. There were the couches with throw pillows in the lobby and the variety of flavored coffee packets in the break room, as well as the coffee cake, which I molested without hassle of any sort. There were the framed diagrams of hydraulic hose fittings on the walls and I still knew every thread and gauge.

A gentle music suggested wind chimes.

And there was Tony on his way to the bathroom! Are you feeling better, Tony asked through crumby whiskers.

I can't remember my answer but I will never forget the look on his face as he came closer, the look of a surgeon swooping down to remove anyone's throat.

PAINTINGS

JULIE GREEN

Page 38. *Gold Standard*, 2019, acrylic, 22k gold leaf, and glow-in-the-dark paint on gessoed Chinet-brand paper plate, 10" × 10" × 0.25". Private collection.

Page 39. *Women's Wrestling*, 2017, acrylic and dayglow paint on paper plate, 10.25" × 10.25" × 1". Private collection.

Page 40. *No, Yes: Azure Wish #102*, 2017, acrylic, glow-in-the-dark paint, and nail polish on Chinet-brand paper plate, 10.25" × 10.25" × 1". Collection of Julia I. Ward, Hailey, Idaho.

Page 41. *I Won't Wear*, 2017, acrylic and dayglow paint on Chinet-brand paper plate, 10.25" × 10.25" × 1". Collection of Heather Grace Gordy & Hasan Elahi, Portland, Oregon.

Page 42. *The Wait Plait*, 2020, acrylic, glow-in-the-dark paint and 22k gold leaf on gessoed Chinet-brand paper platter, 10" × 12.75" × 1". Private collection, New York.

Page 43. *Wishdog*, 2020, acrylic, fabric and 22k gold leaf on gessoed Chinet-brand paper platter, 10" × 12.75" × 0.25". Collection of Lavar Munroe, Baltimore, Maryland.

Page 44. *Gossip Bridles*, 2017, acrylic and glow-in-the-dark paint on Chinet-brand paper plate, 10.25" × 10.25" × 1". Collection of Matthew T. Newton, New York, New York.

Page 45. *Armani for The Colbert Report*, 2017, acrylic and glow-in-the-dark paint on Chinet-brand paper plate, 10.25" × 10.25" × 1". Private collection.

Page 46. *Iowa, a Place to Grow*, 2019, acrylic and glow-in-the-dark paint on gessoed Chinet-brand paper platter, 12.75" × 10" × 0.25". Private collection.

Page 47. *Chanel Cruise Collection*, 2020, acrylic, glow-in-the-dark paint, silver leaf, and palladium leaf on gessoed Chinet-brand paper platter, 12.75" × 10" × 0.25". Private collection.

Page 48. *Retriever Receiver*, 2020, acrylic, glow-in-the-dark paint, wool tweed and 24k gold leaf on Chinet-brand paper plate, 10" × 10" × 1". Collection of the artist.

(All images courtesy of the artist and UPFOR.)

ORGY

DAVE BARRETT

The frenzy he started has sculpted something final into the back
of her brain, the mold she can't jump out of.

GENTLEMEN

DAVE BARRETT

With a church of patience they waited like gentlemen for virility
to blast.

AT HOME

DAVE BARRETT

Walking naked into that soupy house of hers and feeling as if I too was a plucked thing brewing.

GOOD BOOK

DAVE BARRETT

Though some of his chapters she'd skip over entirely it was as simple as her laying her right hand down upon a person and swearing by them almost without ever knowing why and him needing to be sworn upon plus she liked to reuse old things and he liked to feel useful so when she went over to the bench where he sat and right there at the church's own fire sale sewed up his lumpy jacket and uprooted sleeves he became a page turner again.

SMALL BEARDED SPOT

DAVE BARRETT

Even though I wasn't catching any fish and was sinking my lures into a lot of wood I was at least cutting away if not my line my tensions too away from the boat and spent the better part of a very windy day not attached to anything at all but when I decided I was going to come down or more precisely tie up to the pier and walk into the cabin fishless but free I blarneyed over to the pier's edge instead for one more try dropped myself back down and still couldn't pull even the sharpest hooks through the small bearded spot of water.

GENIUS

CULLEN McANDREWS

There's a little jigsaw monk I own. He wears a great brown robe and is made of pieces. My mother put him together from a box, a long time ago. One thousand pieces, she always said, though I find it hard to believe. He's only ten inches tall. The pieces are all there, held just behind the glass, but I've never counted them. It's too arduous a task. For years the monk has hung on the living room wall of the house I grew up in.

I think the puzzle used to be darker, but in August the sun would rise in the south and run in through the casement window onto his intricately painted face that I watch a lot.

It's a small town I live in and there's not much to do in it. For a while I saw a woman who told me to get a job, make some money. I told her that I'd already tried, though I hadn't. I told her that nobody was hiring. Maybe not somebody like you, she replied.

She left me, like you'd expect, but hung around for longer than I was used to.

I went to the front window to examine the thermometer taped up outside. The slim red line of it was quivering between two temperatures I couldn't believe, not at that hour. The sun was shining and the sky was empty and blue like some swollen curd.

Across the street my neighbor Leah's garage door opened. I stepped out into the thick heat and began kicking at clods of dirt chunked out of the ground, hoping to catch her eye. She saw me and waved raggedly. Leah taught little impaired kids down at the local school—kids who couldn't speak English or couldn't read right or couldn't count to ten without standing up and going to the window and hitting it repeatedly. She shouted something at me but I couldn't understand it—from one of the nearby streets came the sound of drag-race driving that I despise, where the little engine levers are whirring so fast it makes a drowning noise—so I just smiled and nodded to her and lifted my hand and made a little thumbs-up and she smiled even wider and got into her car. I watched her drive off. She drove slowly, unerringly, just the way she always did.

I left the house and walked through the front yard, past the hedges already unfurling from their recently clipped cubeness. At the bottom of our hill was a busy road, two lanes running in each direction. The kind of road that exhibits a delusional shimmer in the high sun, headlights twinned in the pavement. Its name was numeric. Cars rolled down it and they didn't slow.

The library was on this road. So was the gas station where I did my shopping. The clerk there, whose name I've forgotten, was a dripping man, all pus and phlegm and sputum. I'd have pitied him if he weren't so perverse. A year before this he caught me with a beer in my pant leg and he hit it with his softball bat so it exploded and soaked my right shoe, which I ended up having to throw out. He made me pay for the beer, too, though I told him I only didn't have any pockets. I'm lucky I drink out of cans.

He smiles when he sees me now, like he has a private little joke I'm not in on. I am in on it. It just isn't funny.

I arrived at the library and found it was closed. A padlocked chain ran through the door handles and a handwritten sign reading EMERGENCY was pasted above them, the scrawl Lutheran in its derangement.

Sitting on the curb was a man I recognized from the library's bathroom, where he shaved himself. I asked if he knew about the emergency, how long it had gone on, but he only shook his head and looked back at the blacktop, softening in the sun.

I squinted at the hill I'd walked down and couldn't face it. There was a twinge in my hamstrings just seeing the tilt. Instead I turned toward Slocum Avenue, the last gasping vestige of a vigorous urban past. In angular letters printed atop some kind of black-and-blue lightning storm, a sign read NEW DIMENSION REALITY CLUB.

Behind me the door shut with some sort of future sound— the sound of a laser or interdimensional portal or another dreamy thing. Despite the exterior shine, the room was dark.

"I don't have any money," I told the man who stood before me.

"Try for free," he said. "We only need a brief scan."

Eventually nothing happened. I sat on a table.

I marked my way home by keying profanities onto the cars that littered the street.

Leah was out in front of her house as I got to mine. She lived alone. Her husband had left her three years ago—something I knew because she'd spent an entire year not mentioning him.

She crossed the road and asked, "Are we still on tonight for drinks? I asked you this morning, you gave me a thumbs-up? Well. If you'd still like to."

Can you imagine a life like this, where everything starts to go your way?

Leah smiled when she ushered me in, but I made a pass, dragged my hand up her leg, and she threw me out. It wasn't what she meant, I guess.

Leah found me once, as I slipped heads of cabbage from the troughs hanging outside of a farmers market.

"I'm still not interested, you must understand," she said.

On the corner, far away, she stopped to shout one more thing at me that I didn't hear.

My desires are small and piddling. Like everyone else, I began masturbating in the library, in the early morning, before it got crowded.

In my own house I smelled something, a stench, fecund and marshy, a smell that drooped.

Just beneath and in front of the monk, on the mantel, was a splayed stain, something in the shape of his body. It was dark, looked like spilled oil.

And that smell I smelled had become strong, like passion.

TRANSFORMATION

HEDGIE CHOI

I used to know someone who didn't (doesn't) like snow globes because they were (are) *fake*. What do you mean? I asked. You shake it and the snow falls but it is the same snow that was already on the ground, she said. Do you know how precipitation works? I asked. In the *real* world, so to speak, do you know where snow comes from? Then that person began becoming not known to me.

LAST NIGHT

HEDGIE CHOI

I spent some time building a life-size horse out of cardboard boxes, an activity that I had thought about doing as a child and put off for two decades. He was crudely made but clearly equestrian and could stand by himself unsupported. I put the horse by the window because I wanted the world to know what I had done. I was pleased with my work, how I had labored briefly but intensely at something of no value or significance and I wanted it to be witnessed by others that they might learn something about me and themselves. Later that night I went to check my mail. As I was returning to the apartment I saw a giant horse through the window and screamed. I screamed at my own horse. It was life-size! It was right by the window! It stood by itself unsupported! God, are you there? Stop screaming. It's me, your horse.

THANK YOU THANK YOU THANK YOU THANK YOU THANK YOU HAVE A NICE DAY

HEDGIE CHOI

I saw a plastic bag blowing across a parking lot and thought of my father who learned about the great snowy owl in school and later that same day saw a white plastic bag for the first time in his life in the sky and thought, *There it is—the owl!* It seems important to point out now that my father once kicked me in the stomach when I was thirteen. But before that I did call him a worthless motherfucker. But before that he brought me into the world. And later he will leave me in it. My thoughts in the parking lot had nothing to do with any of this. My thoughts were of a casual and fond nature.

CHORUS

JONATHAN JOHNSON

"You know I jerked off over a hundred boys and a couple of teachers, too, in high school," she says. She checks her nails. She wonders what our parents would have thought. I tell her they knew.

"So now you know I died," she says. "Of course," she says, going lower.

They could be more careful. But they are not more careful. She feels the weight. The weight grows. The weight grows here and there. Then the weight is uniform. The weight is constant.

"Is this hers?" one says. "Of course it is," says another, which is when she feels them—all of them. They enter her all over.

ACES

CAROL EDELSTEIN

One day we made Ken and Barbie play the slots. Ken was a little off, but Barbie's moon was in jackpot—with forty bucks to start, she had twenty-three hundred by evening. She bought herself a new pocketbook with a beaded clasp, and afterward she treated Ken to the "Sunrise Special" at a 24-hr. breakfast place. Ken was sulky, so next she tried taking him up to their complimentary suite for a relaxing blow job. That went okay, but he was still not all that fun. They ran the hot tub and tried out the jets.

How about a midnight show? said Barbie.

Ken said he'd rather watch some porn.

Well, you can watch it yourself, said Barbie, I'm on a roll. She took off for the lobby. She won three rounds of baccarat while flirting with a guy in a yellow suit, who looked sort of gay.

Jill said, You can't tell who's gay from looking.

Can too.

Mom peeked in. Oh, hi there, Jill. I was just telling your mom what a pleasure you are. I hope you're staying for supper, we're having fish sticks.

Thank you, Mrs. McInerny.

Where are the newlyweds off to now?

The Aces Casino, said Jill. They have a complimentary suite.

Mom giggled. What do you girls know about a casino? Obviously too much!

Barbie's on a winning streak, I told her.

Ken is being a sore loser, added Jill.

Typical guy behavior, said Mom. Your father never likes it when I beat him at slapjack. Supper in ten. Don't forget to wash up.

That night, Jill stayed over and pretended to be asleep when I felt her breasts. It went okay, but she was not all that fun.

EXCERPTS FROM A JOURNAL

September 2, 2000, to September 6, 2001

LYDIA DAVIS

September

"I am going to the funeral, lock up the chicken"

(title of photo by Douglas Curran)

Proust's full name was Marcel-Valentin-Louis-Eugène-Georges Proust

D.F. went to St. Malo and other coastal resorts in summer as a child, with uncles, aunts and cousins, fifteen children, rented house, the children would sleep in a German blockhouse, this was 1946. Brittany was felt to be healthier, not as "sexual" as the Mediterranean, the children were required to swim, taken out in a *canot*, which would then be turned upside down, dumping the children.

Agatha Christie: "He penetrated to the drawing room."
    "it would be their money that had gone West."
    "don't be an oyster!"
    "the general eyed the tantalus sadly" (tantalus=temptation)

dog—a sort of professional interest in certain things on the ground—

No, Mr. President, I could not come to the phone—I was carrying a ladybug out of the house.

The Object in the Blurred Mystery Photo
If it has straight edges, it probably isn't anything intended to be obscene.

Debate over "was" vs. "were." Has turned somewhat unpleasant because copy editor became offended.

Takes many minutes to achieve that casual, friendly tone in the email message. (A minute or two to put that exclamation mark in, another minute or two to take it out.)

putting her moccasins out in the rain
                      (D, about anger and how he expressed it
                      toward S. when he was five years old or so)

Treacle and clotted cream; bread thus spread

A family tradition of looking out the window to see who's arguing in the street.
A family tradition of remembering the worst moments of family life.
A family tradition of finding fault, especially pointing out fat people, of suggesting improvements.

(The thrill of having been there comes over me again and again.)
(This is one of the few times I would use the word "thrill.")

They always did continue (to live), so the rule you understood was that they continued (friends of the family). Then, when they ceased to continue, you could not quite grasp it. Somewhere, you felt, they still continued——   (death)

                                        [on bus]
Ex. of dislocation of common speech and thought: "Outside it was Tuesday." (First line of destroyed novel by David Schubert quoted by J. Ashbery.)

J. Ashbery enjoys Schubert more than Pound or Eliot.

Wallace Stevens: "The poem must resist the intelligence / Almost successfully."

Aposiopesis, the figure of rhetoric which is the uncompleted thought.

The uncompleted thought, the figure of rhetoric called aposiopesis.

aposiopetic

sympathetic, sympathesis

"Outside" immediately suggests to us "inside," as "Tuesday" suggests the other days of the week. But the outdoors itself does not suggest the indoors. Thus the effect of language. Just as "oak fire" suggests more than the oak fire itself, which most of all simply is, in its is-ness, thing-ness, fire-ness—

Beautiful title "Peter and Mother"

Oh God oh where is it, oh it's in my own lap, oh God oh where are they, those cows that are always there behind the billboard thank god, are they gone at last, no, down there beyond another billboard there are two of them anyway fresh and large coming out of the skirt of the woods—

time to sort my thoughts, time to do my accounts, my poor old mother, so stricken to see me go, so stricken, before, to hear that I wouldn't stay longer. Presenting her large face to me—is the lipstick on right, is there powder on my cheeks—this is what I can't see—

the beauty of those long-legged animals, a cow and five horses, the way they stand on the rising and falling land, facing up, facing down, their muscles compensating, beautiful and strong in the sunlight—they are standing relatively still but they are grazing—

the land descends abruptly as if—I suspect a body of running water—Ah, there's the water, a meager little meandering streamlet, muddy, reedy, weedy—

October

One level of sensitivity to language-sounds says "Mother and Peter" sounds wrong; and a higher level of sensitivity (that has developed beyond the first level) is pleased by it.

run under bare poles (sailing term)

brusk, brusque [fr. It. *brusco*, fr. ML *bruscus*, butcher's-broom] [another dict. doesn't agree]

give (of weather): to become mild

Every now and then she had to exercise her right to correspond with him or that right would be lost.

"She put it around my neck. She's dead now. It was a gold

necklace. My daughter took it down to Washington to see what it was worth. It was worth $2,000. My daughter took it and put it in a safe-deposit box. Can't you imagine?"

(V. about gift from employer)

Suzanne, the Way They Often Are   (title)

Carol Gardens   (for name of character)

dog: he takes a professional interest in a boy who may be on the other side of a door (his nose pointed down and ears pointed forward at the door sill)

How alliteration—for instance "maladies and manias"—can make us forgive or overlook a slightly odd word choice.

Bored? Try going around the supermarket in the opposite direction (tip passed on to me by an experienced long-time shopper).

Too private to publish.

[bus Boston to Kingston]
Study of paths, footpaths, and sidewalks. Where you can walk and where you can't—Where you are meant to and where you are not meant to. Where a path has been made for you and where you make your own path.

(Difference between three terms and two terms. Proust's fondness for two terms or even the balance of two pairs of terms. Pairs of two have greater balance and stability, whereas sets of three tend to propel one forward. So in Proust there is resting and balance in the pairs and also forward motion in the threes.)

tactful seagull

Both of two apparently contradictory statements can be true—it only requires shifting or nuancing each by a few degrees—

"I have a perishing thirst!" (woman in Wingate)
perishing   perish the thought

Just me, the bus, and the work—and the other passengers for company (just enough, one every other seat or so), and the pretty fall colors out the window.

Fried filet of sole resting on a folded damask napkin (to absorb the fat) with half a lemon at each corner. (Proust's preferred food?)

(Bus along highway—peaceful because it is so sustained—unending straight line being drawn)

Fried potatoes also served on napkin, well drained.

"His wardrobe was very simple, very correct."   (about Proust)

Took taxis everywhere and never walked except on carpets and parquets. (Proust.) Sounds in "carpets and parquets" (Pleasing phrase for three reasons—image; symmetrical and rhyming sounds; words sitting on line between familiarity and unfamiliarity, meaning and non-meaning.)

"very neat and fast, as he did everything, but with such meticulousness" (Proust)

Céleste wore wooden clogs growing up as a child in Lozère (in the 1890s).

After losing everything in the fire, he borrows the neighbor's hat to go to Mass on Sunday, and the hat is too small.

"I found her in bed, yellow as a lemon."

Wedding. Sympathy. (Categories of greeting cards) (Extend)

(You may work on a piece of writing the way a physical therapist works in an old folks' home: she assembles in the PT room three old people with broken arms, bruised knees, and/or weakened muscles, and works with them alternately, letting them rest in between. (At first I wondered why? Why not take just one into the PT room, why make the others wait? But then, what's wrong with waiting, anyway? And there's the social aspect, too.))

Now one dictionary has attacked and harmed another. (The "old dictionary" coming down on the spine of the Shorter OED and ripping it.) (I do think it was jealous because I had consulted the OED a few times today and I usually do not.)

A bright field picked out by the sun.
picked out

Up late alone downstairs reading articles about nausea and the Sydney Opera House.

Yesterday one of my dictionaries attacked another and tore its spine. Jealousy, pure jealousy. And, even, they should be friends, lying beside each other all the time. Are they perhaps too much together?

"Mature curatorial student"   (from university email)

Money for old rope. (= something for nothing or almost nothing)

And—that old dictionary—it sheds or drops bits of dry yellow old paper from inside its spine so that there is a dust and a litter around it and stuck under the edges of other books, other dictionaries—It cannot quite control its own waste anymore— maybe the time has come to move it out of the house—

prig—martinet
fop or dandy

"I didn't understand a word you said to Sister Theresa!"

(nurse in Dr. Figge's office, to me)

[bus Kingston to NYC]

Now, at the age I am, my sneezes sound like my mother's sneezes, rich, full, vocal.

(V. exciting to me the idea of gems of lyric poems embedded in rougher stuff of Beddoes' *Death's Jest-Book* as described by John A.—that without the rougher stuff, though, it wouldn't work. So—the rough stuff "spoils" or makes imperfect the work as a whole, but is a necessary bed ("magma") for the lyrics—

Stories within stories: French call it a novel with drawers.

Now where was I? (Return to that little bit of weeping I was doing for my father, after interrupting it to translate some Spanish phrases on a store front . . .)

a minor hobby of spotting certain favorite grammatical mistakes and spelling errors.

Ex. of dislocation of usual thought and speech patterns (of usual thinking): "What was that sound we heard / fall on the snow?" (John Wheelwright, quoted by J.A.) "It was a frozen bird. / Why must you know?" First two lines of "Why Must You Know?" There must be a figure of speech that names this displacement.

Displacement or elision: the sound we heard *of something falling* on the snow.

More and more the sense of how we tread a very narrow path of "the accepted" in our writing and thinking. Shd. accumulate examples of what is *outside* our thinking. (That *was* the value of diversity, anyway—exposure to the unknown, unfamiliar.)

Veuve Clicquot—Proust's favorite champagne.

J.A. describes those lines as "slightly askew" and "toying with the reader by keeping even his most straightforward proclamations slightly off balance."

"Poetry" and "prose"—both about hiding, or can be, but hiding in different ways—poetry leaving out, and more obviously cryptic—prose seeming not cryptic, clear and complete on surface but
[bus]
petering
in a kind of petering tremor

their sunburn   (plural possessive w/singular noun)

Gordimer, K. Mansfield, V. Woolf, Hemingway? Relaxed, lingering over descriptions

OED: "mere situation is expressed by '*in* the circumstances,' action takes place '*under* the circumstances.'"

November

mere situation

L.T., punctuation, absence of commas, as in Proust: ". . . each word I choose might indeed be false and what anyway is the meaning or significance of any of it?" (No commas around "anyway.")   (in *Motion Sickness*?)

He opens and shuts as sensitively, immediately and firmly as the valve of a clam or a mussel. (T., aged 12)

Why so funny (in context)?: "I go back to my room and finish *Code Name Mary*."

Perhaps they were both just extremely dehydrated. (couple arguing)

You can look at a book you've been reading and see if it's still "live" like a mine or bomb, or an animal, or if it's dead.

[bus?]

Difference between modifiers separated by "and" and those not.
    "The night is dark and cold and unsympathetic."
    "The night is dark, cold, and unsympathetic."
    "The night is dark, cold, unsympathetic."

berceau, bursar, purser, berth, earth, *Erde*, heir, air

How R. would say just "Yes" or "No" in answer to a question. Everything or anything else he had to say had already been digested into that plain answer. And he couldn't be expected to say more than that. (H. doing a little of this, too, later, from the exhaustion of pain.)

The misapprehension that "chitlins" was an obscenity (in a book banned and confiscated by police).

"What looks like difficulty in her poetry is really accuracy."

Little knobbly things up on the skyline—a distant file of cows—

(That it matters just how a thing is written—a primary identification of writing and thought and then one's own personal identification with that—primum mobile or prima causa.) Then you correct spelling or wording on shopping list or some other thing no one else will ever see.

The spread (like an infection) of the word "exactly" as a one-word response: "Exactly."

pourvu: Ecc. Hist.: incumbent of a living.   (literally, "provided") a meadow enameled with flowers   (old dict.)

primus inter pares

". . . should be committed to work primus inter pares in a loose
governance arrangement . . ."

      (NYIH job description)

. . . to set off for, say, Loyalty Islands . . .

man makes the warps, God sends the woof (Prov.: old dict.)

Distinct sense, as he spoke, that the language moved away from
the subject and into its own creativity, thereby neglecting the
subject or dishonoring the subject; from subject to speaker, as
the language became more elaborate, drew more attention.
(V. important: where attention is)

Should be (mathematically) a one-to-one correlation between
subject, with its requirements, and language conveying it or
commenting on it. When language is 2-to-one or 3-to-one it
begins glorifying itself.

The kitchen trash can with the foot-pedal opener has been on the
whole disappointing.

That painter—maybe I made up for it by tying the shoe of a man
who was very like him.

What concepts are more difficult for the dog: past tense; uncertainty. What are easier: present tense and future tense. The past is no longer possible or real (to him); thus (for people) its identification with fiction. If I say "Maybe we'll go out," and then we don't go out, to him I am saying "we'll go out" and then we don't go out, so "maybe" is the word that signals that what seems real or true is not real or true.

Sparagmos: Gk. ritual rending of the flesh. (email from M.D.)

How context can dull the effect of the lines. (Which is why I enjoy fragments, fragmentation, disjunction). Ashbery book—pieces of poems in a different context, the suspense of awaiting them; the gratification of the whole poem—(And why lines quoted in dictionary are so wonderful.)

A line of gray dust in the fold of her ceramic skirt.

I saw, out of the corner of my eye, that thick, long white thing that had come up over the edge of the page, and a little tremor of fear went through me before I looked straight at it and recognized that it was my own thumb.

I've done my duty at home / and can go away

Why do we suspect she's crazy? Arrangement and rearrangement, coat off and on and off and on.

talented strange stories—either she will be a good writer or will go crazy (she went crazy)

"I have to go home and pay some bills. Please don't be mad at me." She looked mad.
   (Husband and wife at NYU reading.)

She once praised him for a subordinate clause—

I liked his tie but he seemed not alive anymore.
An interesting truth or an uninteresting truth?

window, wind-eye; does eye = hole?

Words still having meaning but being on the edge of incoherence—because the incoherent cry carries the most emotion.

Correlation (mathematically): actually prefer 3-to-one of reality-to-language and 1-to-three of language-to-reality in reader's mind. The words of a poem being the condensed matter that explodes in the reader's mind. The work of condensation or rather compression of experience from writer's experience to writer's words—

December

Metaphor in "brilliant" [from L. *berillus*, beryl]; metaphor in Fr.

septentrion, "north" (the direction where the seven stars lie). So that "in the direction of the seven stars" has been condensed into *septentrion*; and "as bright as a beryl" has been condensed into "brilliant."

Chaudhuri's lack of commas. Openness of that.

I have an idea of what I'd like to be like . . .

"shelf supper"   (from *Fannie Farmer*)
"The food is bad, but every day there is something I can eat and even like."   (version of L.T. message)

"It doesn't even lack that slight touch of the grotesque which is an essential part of all great works."   (Proust about Hardy's *The Well-Beloved*, which he loved.)

January 2001

Want to write Proust piece about his relationship with trees.

In all these weeks away from work, have only learned not to put commas around "however."
Over the Christmas holidays, I learned only one thing—not to put commas around "however."

Maladie du scrupule: morbid irresolution

Proust uses the word "amphibology" in a letter to Scott Moncrieff. "The intended amphibology of *Temps perdu* . . ." (Tadié, p. 770)

Amphibology: ambiguity in language; a phrase or sentence ambiguous because of its grammatical construction

The Doctor's Advice. If you're not getting out of breath, find a higher mountain. (Dr. W.)

agony column

Invention of the Cross (in the old days, "invention" could also mean "discovery" or "finding")

Typo in translation: "drink a bup of tea."

To be cut for the stone (read that somewhere and then found it in the old dictionary): to be operated on for gallstone

one sandwich short of a picnic (expression for person who's not "all there")

if it's nothing but a cabbage head

dog: smells my hand, not sure what is on it, possibly interesting, then licks it out of a general principle—

drop off the twig = die

Is it wrong to want to be comfortable and try to be comfortable—morally wrong? Just how comfortable should one try to be? I.e. at what point is one wrong to try to be more comfortable? (Thoughts that come up when riding on the bus, a little uncomfortable. Or at other times when uncomfortable.)

Rest Rooms of Albany   (sign on side of nice new blue van)
(driver of car, seen from the bus:) Hamburger in one hand, reaching into bag of french fries with the other, no hand on the wheel

V. says: gravy so good that you put up a note on the door saying nobody's home.

"You'll have to have a quiet sarsaparilla with the guy." (A. about meeting with D.E.)

February

"Ye stiff-necked and of uncircumcised hertes and eares" (Tyndale, *Acts* 7.51)

"Drink no longer water, but use a little wine for thy stomach's sake and thine often infirmities." (*1 Timothy*, 5:23)

Father & Son Moving & Storage

Bob stirring his tea about 1½ times as fast as I, or 1⅔. And are all his other motions as much faster than mine?

"the whole shehoot" or "the whole shoot"—V. quoting her grandmother—meaning the neighborhood or vicinity—

That almost pathologically hesitant man (calling about the O. yearbook). Then "warming to his subject" he began to speed up a bit—the hesitations were still there, but intervals were shortened slightly—

I could show more enthusiasm over large appliances—and small appliances too!

. . . though the judges particularly commended the placement of one birch.   (for "Good Taste Contest")

March

I sigh and a piece of dust moves over the desk. (shifts and rests)

You have to talk to the audience a little to show them you like them (and you do like them)—just enough to show that—

That nothing's off-limits to think or to write, but some things are off-limits to publish because they would do some kind of damage.

April

(That name on the radio, misheard: "A spokesman for the White House, Pregnant Shoulder . . .")

He likes to see me paying a bill. (It reassures.)

She had to face it: she was not well groomed! She was not a well groomed person! (Usually realized this under the bright lights and in the clean rooms of the dentist's office.)

Steal the wind from a vessel

Can feel my bottom wearing out—at this work.

Think how swiftly and efficiently dreams compose narratives out of the material stored in our brains: if I am half waking, in the morning, my dream composes a college campus, several buildings—realistic—, some sort of reception, other women, men, and a young administrator who tells me there aren't any ladies' rooms in that building because only men work there.

May

The simple freedom of allowing myself to write a contraction.

Scrubbing a cutting board makes the word "Saratoga."

This morning he compared me to a car battery. "You're like a car battery," he said. (Because I asked him to buy distilled water for me.)

V. reports that her pastor said to her: "You were made when they said, 'Let's make 'em!'"

Nice to share a love—all to love the same thing/person   (the many Proust fan clubs)

Sorry, Mom, but I am treating my husband with more respect now. (I know it's not what you would wish—) (not what you taught me)

dog—I lean down to scold him and he lifts his muzzle to smell my breath—

"nice, tidy family"   (from email ad)

R.S. word: *sitzfleisch*—ability to sit still for a long time (and do one thing?)

June

Because I'm looking at her, I think I look as normal as she looks.

And the closer she gets to being all ready, the worse she looks.

(woman preparing to go out on date—was this the one I saw putting on makeup on bus?)

[Banyuls, France]

Older woman attached to hotel who drags little English bulldog along by his harness or hauls him dangling in the air. (Mother of owner.)

July

Pitcher of water taken from *source/fontaine* in street outside restaurant—

Slab or round of goat cheese w/warm honey and slivered almonds—

Wine meant only to go with anchovies—we were advised that one would order it only if five people were having anchovies (one glass each).

Mayonnaise: books made out of pieces of other books (M. Costes said that word—I think that was what he meant).

[bus to Albany]

When the beginning of the final servitude feels like the beginning of freedom. (Just as the beginning of the last action before the execution feels like the beginning of the execution.)

Then I begin thinking a good deal about water.

Ever since translating the image in Proust, I am looking at circles of shade under little trees at midday.

Sometimes certain things loom as important; then they slide away into the middle distance and are not so important (e.g. opinions of me held by certain people).

August

"The men went into another room and had the nuts and sherry or whatever they have. The only place the women could go was up a ladder into a sort of toilet . . ."   (Mother)

in theory I don't think he should say Fuck You to me, but in fact . . .

Another acknowledgment: thanks to N.M. for the expressions "dog's breakfast" and "summer-complaint." Thanks to L.T. for the word "moron." Thanks to L.S. for a new sense of the present participle.

September

"Go light the snails," she said.   (clay snails Mother gave me.)

Patches of insensitivity (in R.), as in patches of fog or patches of skin disease

Always carry pair of socks when traveling; always carry one or two teabags.

The fact that he is eating Cheese Doritos is a temporary problem; whereas that other man snorting is more likely to be an ongoing problem.   (potential seatmates on bus)

_____

These journal excerpts have not been edited. They remain as they were originally set down, complete with misspellings and inconsistent punctuation (or punctuation that has a logic of its own).

I AM BRILLIANT

DEB OLIN UNFERTH

In my bright dress and buckled shoes, I was fearsome last night. If only I could be today the person I was last night.

I started with a joke about myself, did a little dance with my hands, and how my friends laughed!

There'd been cheers (well, maybe not cheers). Matt said, *You're brilliant! That was so fun!*

But now it's morning and I am not the person I was last night. She was not to be found, either, when I interviewed for that job I wanted. Never attends family gatherings.

But if I was her more often (I console myself), I would have to *be her*, steer by her choices, carry on with the illuminated life she would have built for the two of us, which would be exhausting, and I don't think I'd be up for it.

PEARLINE CLEANS UP

SUSAN LAIER

As a member of the privileged class and high society, Pearline is accustomed to garden parties, luncheons, and fancy dinners.

One afternoon a neighbor drops by to help Pearline prepare for that evening's dinner party. Pearline asks her to please sweep the floor and points to the closet where the broom is kept. When the neighbor opens the closet door, a pile of magazines and other items fall out. Then she notices there is a haphazardly stacked combination of dishes, rugs, pillows, and other miscellany behind a couch. She begins catching glimpses of little heaps of odds and ends behind doors and other furniture. So she good-naturedly asks Pearline, "What is going on?"

Pearline confesses she just ran out of time to do a real cleaning so she swept the heaps of clutter out of sight. There is more on the back porch and some in the kitchen pantry.

"I've made a wonderful dinner, however. Let's set the table. Here's the tablecloth," she says, handing the neighbor a stack of collectible china plates. All the guests agree the dinner is fabulous and no one mentions the hidden messes, including the messes in the crannies of Pearline's mind.

The food is too good—veal à la king, the golden feather cake, although the pineapple date salad was underwhelming.

YOUNG LUST

SUSAN LAIER

He invited her to join him upstairs in the barn, to enjoy the room he had just remodeled. It had a pool table, a dart board, pretty furniture, and an old record player. He started spinning a pile of antique 78 records and some 45s too. After hearing several of them, she was delighted to recognize a familiar selection from her childhood. "Suzy Snowflake" by Rosemary Clooney played, with its bouncy tempo and juvenile words. She giggled, explaining that this was a song she listened to over and over again when she was just a kid. She even made up dances to go with it.

As she listened to the song now she mimicked the words that were still alive in her memory. She even acted out her little-girl dance steps. She begged him to play it again and again.

Her performance ruined his interest in her, and his amorous thoughts, afterward, turned more toward Bonnie Dorsky.

BODY OR SOUL

SUSAN LAIER

There were three of us on the date that night: Ellen, her brother Owen, and me. Owen had wanted a date with me for a long time and finally Ellen fixed us up. She did it in a way that she could come too. That was fine with me because Owen just wanted to drink beers while Ellen and I danced.

We invented a sideways "mashed potatoes" step that went perfectly to the blues-funk rock and roll being played that night at the Show Boat. The Show Boat was a bar–dance club venue that was shaped like a boat. It looked just like a boat sitting in the parking lot behind the bank.

Owen eventually passed out in the corner of the booth where he sat, while Ellen and I exhausted ourselves between beer binge- ing and trips to the ladies' room.

I loved that night.

I am wondering these days, Did I ever come back to life?

WHY DID SHE DO IT?

SUSAN LAIER

Joe and Michele married. Because Joe was a rogue priest who had given up the priesthood, marriage was a novel and exciting experience for him, especially to the beautiful flower child Michele. They enjoyed several years of lewd parties, experimenting with psychedelics, and swimming naked with friends in nearby streams. Life was fabulous while Joe was younger.

Thirty years her senior, Joe naturally aged before Michele. She grew restless, wanting to travel and try new things. Joe could not join her for one reason or another, so Michele thought it best that they get divorced. However, Joe begged her to continue to be his wife. He advised her, "Go and do whatever you want but please do not divorce me." He offered to pay her expenses: travel, lodging, even a house of her own if she wanted.

He gave her cars. He took care of all her financial needs for years. So she was able to pursue her passion for boating and, oddly enough, she became the captain of a tugboat. She loved the independence and adventure.

As Joe got older he became more feeble, and Michele didn't want to, but she returned to her husband. Their relationship is now more like that of father-daughter, or even grandfather-granddaughter. She stays with him, all the while yearning to go back to her tugboat life on the huge waterways that surround and invade the Americas.

Joe loves her so much he ignores her yelling at him and calling him names.

She complained to a neighbor about the whole thing. The neighbor asked her, "Why, why do you do it?"

"Why do I do it?" Michele began, and this gave her the first opportunity to tell her story, which she finds is a pleasure that can satisfy her regularly.

A GROWN-UP MAN

SUSAN LAIER

Daryll is an eighth grader who is in love with his teacher. Really she is a study hall aide who is teaching him and others how to make a braided leather bracelet and belt. She's showing her craft to the students and Daryll loves it and her.

Sometimes Daryll rides his bike to the aide's home, which is six miles away. He loves to talk to her and offers to show her things in nature he has discovered like waterfalls and animal homes. He invites her to his house to meet his pet raccoon and to see the huge cage that is its home. The family has a pet lamb that comes into the house and everyone takes a turn feeding it with a baby bottle.

Toward the end of the school year, Daryll insists that his study hall teacher go to the movies with him. She finally agrees and of course she drives. They go to see *Butch Cassidy and the Sundance Kid*. Daryll acts like a grown-up man and pays for everything. The teacher is impressed.

For some reason she always compares any date she has in the future with this "date," and it is hard to find one who provides equal respect and has such incredibly good manners.

WHAT IS THIS?

SUSAN LAIER

I heard myself complain to no one. It's unnatural, it's drab. I am lonely for others even though they, too, may be dull. Snow has partially covered the lawn and various surrounding fields, as if it is a big gingersnap cookie decorated with white frosting.

DREW ONLY STAYS AN HOUR

KIM CHINQUEE

Drew only stays an hour. He's checking his phone. He says he still has patients.

Mike's a cyclist who doesn't wait for me on the ride. He had to leave on his airplane to negotiate a deal at the last minute. I asked if we'd keep in touch, and because I'd asked more than once, he said that made him feel unsettled. I'd spent nights while he was away, walking his property.

We fucked more than once. We fucked more than twice and three times.

He made me lots of coffee.

There's a judge, lots of cyclists, a banker. I've opened up my range.

I'm sensible. I'm a professor. A triathlete, with friends.

The CEO comes to my house again. I'm selective about the men who I have sex with.

Since Mike flew off on his plane, I wonder where he is. He said to me, when we started talking a year ago—we were mostly off at first for many months because he found somebody else— he just wants to fall in love again. After one of my recent visits, he said he told his kids about me. They're grown. This man is in his sixties.

I thought I was starting to fall in love with him, when he said he had to get on his plane again. He has not been in touch since he landed two days ago. Or maybe it's been three?

I wake, after a date with the banker, with a backache. He lives in a high-rise. It wasn't our first date. His apartment is large and minimalist, and his open closet reveals plenty of suits that clearly come from the cleaners. He went golfing with the city mayor over the weekend. He brags about these things. He walks around before me without clothes on.

He serves me. I sip from my cup, fold my legs, and notice the city buildings, so tall and solid, surrounded by the fog. I tell the banker what a great time I had last night.

I was a cop once in the air force. I aimed my rifle once. I never arrested anyone.

I STILL HAVEN'T TOLD THE STORY I MEANT TO TELL

CLANCY MARTIN

We were a very poor family and like all poor families knew who had what and how.

How you steal a book-size magazine or any book is much more difficult than most things you might shoplift. Books are a hard-to-hide size, heavy, prominent. A record you can slide between other records and into a bag. A magazine, same way. Clothes are easiest of all because they fit under your clothes. Casual secrecy is how you shoplift most things. Just be quick and sly: people are distracted and also mostly reluctant to bust you. But my technique for books took courage. This is what I did. I walked in reading a book while wearing my backpack. It was always a new book. Usually I had written my name across the pages opposite the spine, the fore edge, to make it as prominent as possible. I'd keep a pen in the book. Then I'd find the *Paris Review* or whatever. I'd find a few books, sit down in the aisles, read a bit. I'd write my name on the new *Paris Review*. I'd put the book I'd walked in with into my backpack and the other books back on the shelves, walk out reading the *Paris Review*. If stopped, which I was, more than once, I'd just say oh I came in with this. If they doubted me, which also happened a couple of times, I'd show them I had my name on all my books, which I did, even in grad school.

Once a friend of mine, Pierre Lamarche, now a phil professor at UVU in Utah, looked at the books in the office we shared and asked me, does your mom sew your name in your underwear too? He didn't understand that I'd been using this technique to get my books for years. I used it through junior high school and high school and even in college bookstores. I used it in Half Price Books in Austin. Eventually I used a Sharpie because it was faster and more conspicuous, and I learned I could write my name, put it back on the shelf, and return to carry it out later. At Half Price Books they knew what I was up to and more than once told me, you can't come in here with a book. But I continued.

When I was in junior high at Rideau Park School in Canada I used to take the bus downtown to a bookstore in the mall where I would steal my copy of the *Paris Review*. I read the whole thing back then, keeping it in my backpack, and then threw it away so that my mom wouldn't ask me how I got it.

I've never published there, and a woman I was dating in New York—when we were winding down but not quite through with each other—she called me at my office and asked me if I had read the latest issue. I said yes I had, because by this time I was a subscriber and also had insisted that my university library carry a subscription. She said, that new story—did you read that one?—it's brilliant. I knew the one she meant. I said yes I read that one and I felt like the author was still hiding something. She said no, that was why it was so good, it's what every woman feels like. I said the narrator is a boy. She said yeah, but whatever, it's a cover-up, it happened to the writer. I said yeah, that's what I'm saying, something more happened that she didn't tell us. She said you always think you know things about what the writer was thinking but nobody knows. Not even the writer. I said well, you're the editor.

At this time I was also secret-drinking and the woman I was dating was my editor at a magazine. At last I can be honest about this relationship. She was young and seemed to have enormous sexual enthusiasm but we were both faking our interest in each other because we were so unhappy. She had told me she was in love with someone else, a friend of ours. I wanted only to believe that other possibilities were still before me, that I hadn't already closed all the doors to future changes.

This was complicated because she was my editor and the man she loved was the editor of the *Paris Review* who used to be my editor. So at this time I was suspicious of editors.

Later, the writer of the story in question (who was an editor at a different magazine) interviewed me, and then we fell in love over Facebook and texts, and then we were married, and now we are parents together.

I still haven't told the story I meant to tell. Before I became the writer and the professor who could tell his college library to subscribe to a magazine, but after high school and college, I owned some jewelry stores. And at that time I was addicted to cocaine and owned a Glock and tried to shoot myself in the mouth every morning. It was never a habit. It was a resolution, which I daily failed. It was the saddest and most self-loathing time in my fifty-four years, including my childhood, which was, as the song says, "hell. Hell is for children." Not to be maudlin. But at that time I was also taking speed in the afternoons and evenings so that I could stay awake long enough, after I got off at my jewelry store around 7 p.m., to go check on the wine bar I owned on McKinney in Dallas. And between the jewelry store and the wine bar, sometimes I'd stop at home to write. I wrote more than a hundred stories at this time, often three or four in a night. That was twenty-three years ago, and I still want to tell the story I want to tell.

PAGEANT AT THYATIRA

DARRELL KINSEY

The pageant at Thyatira could be hard to understand. It was more or less a drag show, but it was organized by the church, and no one thought of it as a drag show the way drag shows are now thought of. The families who came to watch each year were fundamentalist families and mountain families who probably did not believe in drag shows, and the men who participated most likely did not believe in them either. They were lawyers and rangers and mechanics and carpenters. They were the men of the church, and no one much wondered what fantasies the pageant might fulfill for them. As far as everyone was concerned, their performance was a straightforward comedy, but it had been a good decade since I had been to see the show. I went again this spring because my older brother, Micah, had decided to participate.

I found Micah in the fellowship hall, where the men were putting the final touches on their outfits. The scene was lively. Many of the wives were helping their husbands and having a fine time cackling and surrounding each man as he was made up. All the voices and the commotion and the caustic smell of cosmetics gave the fellowship hall the feeling of a crowded salon, but Micah was somewhat removed from the activity. He sat in a metal folding chair in the back of the room, and the pink gown he had chosen from the thrift store was far more demure than the floral silks and gaudy designs worn by the other men. Micah was also the only contestant who did not require the fakery of a wig. More than two years he had gone without cutting his hair, and it seemed just as much time had passed without his using a brush. I worked several minutes helping him arrange the strands. We were eventually able to tease the loose pieces in a way that hid the tangles and the clumps. Then there was the question of his beard. All we could do was decorate it with several handfuls of glitter. Next I applied his makeup. I had never applied makeup to anyone before. "Go like this," I said. I painted his lips and outlined them with a dark pencil. I used blush on his cheeks and a smoky shadow across his eyelids. He asked what I thought. I told him he was the sweetest little lady I had ever seen.

The truth was that I had been meaning to come back to Thyatira for several months. I had a reason other than the pageant: there was some news I needed to share with Micah. I wanted him to hear from me, before finding out through other channels, that I had gotten into a serious relationship with Neva Formwaldt, a young woman he himself had dated several years back. I knew Neva had been important to him, and I knew he had not been in another relationship since their breakup. My hope was that the festivities surrounding the pageant would help dispel any kind of difficult feelings between us.

The light of day amplified the garishness of the men's costumes, and in their heels they wandered like the creatures of a carousel let loose from their mechanism. They veered off through the laurels to the back of the pavilion that was filled with the fragrance of caramel corn and funnel cake.

The emcee came to the microphone and introduced the men using variant names. Micah was Meeka. David was Davinia. Jason was Jacinta. They swiveled in quarter turns and shuffled with small steps. They posed, and, not realizing they should pantomime the blowing of kisses, many of them ended up with smeared mouths and printed palms.

During the talent portion of the pageant, one of the elders scraped a fiddle. Then Micah had his turn. His talent was to recite lists of stars that make up some of our more famous constellations. Rigel, Betelgeuse, Bellatrix, Saiph, Alnitak, Alnilam, Mintaka. No one knew whether he had succeeded or failed. I felt bad for Micah, and I was surprised by the level of my disappointment when one of the other fellows was crowned with a tiara.

·   ·   ·

Not until we were sitting in the tall grass outside Micah's trailer was I able to tell him about Neva. My voice was thin, but I was making myself clear.

Micah was always a timid and careful person; my fear was not that he would try to harm me physically. I doubted he would even raise his voice. I kept talking as he sat there tangling his fingers in his beard, causing all the glitter to land in his lap. He smiled. He shifted himself onto his hands and knees and started crawling slowly toward me. I asked what he was doing. He told me to hush. He said everything was fine. "I'm so happy for you," he said. He kept crawling toward me. He hung his arm around my neck. I gathered that he wanted to start touching me and wrestling with me. Maybe it was impossible to share through words the way he was feeling. For several seconds we made a ceremony of rolling and wrestling together. We wrestled in a celebratory way. We wrestled to reach each other the way we did when we were young. Then he climbed on top of me. He had to hike the hem of his gown to straddle me. He held my shoulders to the ground, and he hovered his face over mine. "I'm so glad for you," he said.

SMALL ENVIRONMENTAL CHANGES (LIGHT, ETC.)

VIJAY KHURANA

And ever since then I have been like a small creature in a fable, who recognized his smallness but not quite in time, who lies crumpled beneath the nest and whose eyes are milky and who can barely breathe.

But this was months ago. At some point I fell from Lydia's loft bed, broke a vintage lamp, and injured my arm badly enough to need an X-ray, which in German is named after its discoverer, Wilhelm Röntgen.

BLAST

KAYLA BLATCHLEY

We all teased him, one cop, Buddy.

He had a wide mouth, wide face. A bowl haircut, with the woven shorts and shirt, playing with sticks in the park like a magician.

He wasn't kissing us as much. We looked at his penis in our hands and rubbed with our thumbs the part he said.

We'd go back to the McDonald's and laugh.